THE SECRET GARDEN

The *Oxford Progressive English Readers* series provides a wide range of reading for learners of English.

Each book in the series has been written to follow the strict guidelines of a syllabus, wordlist and structure list. The texts are graded according to these guidelines; Grade 1 at a 1,400 word level, Grade 2 at a 2,100 word level, Grade 3 at a 3,100 word level, Grade 4 at a 3,700 word level and Grade 5 at a 5,000 word level.

The latest methods of text analysis, using specially designed software, ensure that readability is carefully controlled at every level. Any new words which are vital to the mood and style of the story are explained within the text, and reoccur throughout for maximum reinforcement. New language items are also clarified by attractive illustrations.

Each book has a short section containing carefully graded exercises and controlled activities, which test both global and specific understanding.

The Secret Garden

Frances Hodgson Burnett

Hong Kong

Oxford University Press

Oxford

Oxford University Press

Oxford   New York
Athens   Auckland   Bangkok   Bombay
Calcutta   Cape Town   Dar es Salaam   Delhi
Florence   Hong Kong   Istanbul   Karachi
Kuala Lumpur   Madras   Madrid   Melbourne
Mexico City   Nairobi   Paris   Singapore
Taipei   Tokyo   Toronto

and associated companies in
Berlin   Ibadan

Oxford is a trade mark of Oxford University Press

This adaptation first published 1994
This impression (lowest digit)
3   5   7   9   10   8   6   4   2

Retold by Kieran McGovern

Illustrated by K.Y. Chan

Syllabus designer: David Foulds

Text processing and analysis by Luxfield Consultants Ltd

ISBN 0 19 586634 7

Printed in Hong Kong
Published by Oxford University Press (China) Ltd
18/F Warwick House East, Taikoo Place, 979 King's Road,
Quarry Bay, Hong Kong

CONTENTS

CONTENTS

AN ENGLISH GIRL IN INDIA

Mary Lennox

When Mary Lennox was a young girl, she lived in
India. Her father was working for the government
there. She was a sick little child, but her parents did
not really try to look after her. Her father was often ill   5
himself, while her tall, beautiful mother was only
interested in going to parties with her friends.
Mrs Lennox had not wanted a little girl at all. The day
Mary was born, Mrs Lennox told one of the servants
that she wanted to see the child as little as possible.   10

So Mary had her own special servant, or 'Ayah' as
they said in India. Her Ayah dressed her and
undressed her and did everything for her. Because
she never felt well, Mary was very
selfish. She also had a terrible
temper. When she did not
get what she wanted, she
would cry and scream
until someone
gave it to her.

All the servants were afraid of Mary, and nobody liked her.

One very hot morning, when she was nine years old, Mary woke up feeling tired and angry. She became really angry when she saw the servant who stood by her bed. The servant was not her Ayah.

The missing servants

'Why did you come?' she said to the strange woman. 'I will not let you stay. Send me my Ayah.'

The woman looked frightened.

'She cannot come,' whispered the woman.

This made Mary show her bad temper. The little girl screamed and kicked the servant. But the poor woman repeated that the Ayah could not come as she hurried away.

There was something strange happening in the house that morning. Many of the servants were missing, and those who Mary saw all looked very afraid. But no one would tell her anything, so Mary went out to play under the tree in the garden.

From where she was, she could see her mother talking to a young soldier. Suddenly there was a terrible cry. It was coming from the part of the house where the servants lived.

'What is it? What is it?' asked Mary's mother.

'Someone has died,' answered the soldier. 'The terrible sickness, cholera, has come to this house. You should have left here two weeks ago.'

'I know!' cried Mrs Lennox. 'I only stayed to go to that silly party. How foolish I was!'

Mrs Lennox looked very frightened. Mary watched her mother pull the soldier's arm.

'Come with me!' she said to the soldier. Then she turned and ran into the house.

The sickness

After that, terrible things happened. Mary learned that her Ayah had become ill during the night. The servants were crying because she had just died. The next day three more servants died and the others ran away. All over the house and the garden were dying people. Mary ate some fruit and biscuits that she found. Then she fell asleep.

During the second day of the cholera, Mary hid herself in the nursery and was forgotten by everybody.

All through the night she slept. When she woke up, the house was completely silent. Mary waited in her room for somebody to come for her, but her only visitor was a snake. The snake came under the door.

'How strange and quiet it is,' Mary said to herself. 'Perhaps there is nobody in the house but me and the snake.' Almost the next minute she heard voices. 'How terrible!' she heard one voice say. 'That beautiful woman is dead. I think the child is too. I heard there was a child, though nobody ever saw her.'

There is no one left

Mary was standing in the middle of the nursery when someone opened the door. It was a soldier and he looked completely surprised when he saw her.

5 'Barney!' he cried out to his friend. 'There is a child here! A child alone! In a place like this! Who is she?'

'I am Mary Lennox,' the little girl said. 'I fell asleep when everyone had the cholera. Why does nobody come?'

10 The young man whose name was Barney looked at her very sadly. 'Poor child!' he said. 'There is nobody left to come.'

It was in that strange and sudden way that Mary found out about the death of her mother and father.

15 Everyone had either died or left the house. That was why the house was so quiet. Nobody had remembered Mary. There was no one in the house but herself and the snake.

Mary goes to England

20 There was no one left to look after Mary in India, so she was sent to live with her uncle in England. The wife of a soldier travelled with her on the long journey across the sea.

'Where am I going?' Mary asked.

25 'To live with your uncle, Mr Archibald Craven,' said the woman kindly. 'They say he lives in a big house called Misselthwaite Manor. I'm sure you'll like it there.'

At the railway station in London, one of the
30 servants from Misselthwaite Manor came to meet Mary. Her name was Mrs Medlock. She was a fat

woman with very red cheeks and black eyes. She wore a purple dress and a black hat with purple flowers. Mary did not like her, but she almost never liked anyone. And it was clear that Mrs Medlock did not like Mary.

'What an ugly little girl she is!' she said to the soldier's wife. 'And we heard that her mother was beautiful.'

'Perhaps she will improve as she grows older,' said the woman. 'She does look so pale and thin and she never smiles. But children can change so much.'

Mrs Medlock looked again at Mary. The little girl had a thin face and a thin little body. Even her hair was thin and yellow.

'She will have to change a lot,' she answered. 'And there's nothing to improve children at Misselthwaite.'

The two women did not realize that Mary was listening to what they were saying. But Mary had heard every word. She wanted to know more about her uncle and the house he lived in. What sort of place was it? What would he be like?

ACROSS THE MOOR

A strange place

Mrs Medlock and Mary said goodbye to the soldier's wife and got on their train. They sat opposite each other on the train and looked at each other. Mary had nothing to read or to look at. She sat and held her thin little hands together on her dress. She was wearing black gloves and her black dress made her look paler than ever.

Mrs Medlock thought that Mary was the most spoiled-looking child she had ever seen. She watched her for a few minutes, then she began to talk.

'Do you know anything about your uncle?'

'No,' said Mary.

'You never heard your mother or your father talk about him?'

'No,' said Mary. Her mother and father had never talked to her about anything.

'Well, I will say something — to prepare you. You are going to a strange place.'

Mrs Medlock waited for Mary to ask her about this, but the little girl said nothing.

'It's a big dark place, miles from anywhere,' continued Mrs Medlock, 'and it is 600 years old. The house has nearly 100 rooms, though most of them are shut and locked. There're pictures and fine old things that have been there for years. Around the house is a big park with gardens and trees.' She stopped to breathe. 'But there is nothing else,' she ended suddenly.

Mary had begun to listen. It all sounded so different from India, and anything new interested her. But she did not want to look as if she was interested. So she sat still and said nothing.

The man with a crooked back

'Well,' said Mrs Medlock, 'what do you think about that?'

'Nothing,' Mary answered. 'I know nothing about such places.'

Mrs Medlock laughed in a cruel way. 'You are like an old woman. Don't you care?'

'It doesn't matter,' said Mary, 'what I think.'

'You are right there,' said Mrs Medlock. 'I don't know why they are sending you to Misselthwaite Manor. He is not going to care about you! He never cares about anyone.' She shook her head. 'He's got a crooked back. That's what made him go wrong. He was an unhappy young man, even though he had his big house and all his money. Then he got married.'

Mary looked at Mrs Medlock in surprise. She thought it strange that a man with a crooked back would get married.

'She was a sweet, pretty thing,' continued Mrs Medlock, 'and he would have walked across the world to get her anything she wanted. When she died —'

5 'Oh! Did she die?' said Mary without meaning to.

'Yes, she died,' Mrs Medlock answered. 'And it made him stranger than ever. He cares about nobody. He won't see people. Most of the time he goes away, and when he is at Misselthwaite, he shuts himself
10 away in his room.'

It sounded like something in a book, and it made Mary feel a little lonely. A house with 100 rooms nearly all shut up and with their doors locked. A house miles from anywhere. A man with a crooked
15 back who locked himself in his room. She stared out of the window and saw that it was starting to rain.

'There will not be anyone there to talk to you. You'll have to play alone and look after yourself. You'll be told which rooms you can go into, and
20 there are many gardens.'

Mary continued to stare out into the rain. It looked as if it would go on for ever. She watched it until her eyes grew heavy and she fell asleep.

The drive across the moor

25 Mary slept for a long time. When she woke up, it was dark and the train had stopped. Mrs Medlock was shaking her.

'Come on,' she said. 'We're at Thwaite Station. Now we've got a long drive across the moor.'

30 The station was a small one, and nobody but themselves got out of the train. By the entrance a man was waiting with a coach and horses. It was still

raining and the water was falling down the driver's hat and raincoat. He helped them put their bags into the coach and then they drove off.

'What is a moor?' said Mary suddenly.

'Look out of the window in about ten minutes and you'll see,' Mrs Medlock answered. 'We've got to drive five miles across the moor before we get to the house. You won't see much because it is dark.'

Mary looked out of the window. The lights of the coach lit up a little of the road in front of them, and she saw that they were passing through a small village. She could see the church and a little shop window full of toys and sweets. Then they went on to a high road, and she saw bushes and trees. After that, there seemed to be nothing different for a long time.

At last the horses began to go more slowly as they moved up a hill. Soon there were no more bushes and no more trees. Now Mary could see nothing: it was completely dark. The wind made a strange sound.

'We're on the moor now,' said Mrs Medlock.

'It's not the sea, is it?' said Mary.

'No. It's just miles and miles and miles of wild land. Nothing grows on it but wild flowers. Nothing lives on it but wild horses and sheep.'

On and on they drove in the dark. The rain stopped but the wind continued to make strange sounds. The road went up and down, and Mary felt that the journey would never end.

'I don't like it,' she said to herself.

MISSELTHWAITE MANOR

A strange old house

At last Mary saw a light in the distance. They passed through some park gates, and then drove for two more miles down a road with trees on either side. Then they came to the longest house that Mary had ever seen. It was not very high, but it seemed as long as the village they had passed through. There were hundreds of windows, but only one was lit.

A servant opened a large door and showed them into a great entrance hall. It was badly lit. Mary looked very small and strange in her black dress. And she felt small and lost and strange.

'Take the girl to her room,' said the servant to Mrs Medlock. 'He doesn't want to see her.'

Mrs Medlock led Mary up the stairs and down a long corridor. They then went up more steps and down another corridor until they came to a door.

'Well, here you are!' said Mrs Medlock, opening the door. 'This room and the one next to it are where you'll live. Don't go into the other rooms!'

Mary looked around and saw a dark room with a fire in it. There was some food on a table. She felt sure that she would not like living in this room.

Martha

When Mary opened her eyes in the morning, she saw
that a young woman had come into the room. Mary
watched her lighting the fire for a few moments, and
then began to look around her. She had never seen   5
such a strange and sad room. Through a large
window, she could see a great climbing piece of land
with no trees on it.

'What is that?' she said, pointing out of the window.

Martha, the young servant, got to her feet and   10
walked to the window.

'That's the moor,' she said. 'Do you like it?'

'No,' answered Mary. 'I hate it.'

'That's because you are not used to it,' Martha said,
going back to the fire. 'You will like it.'   15

'Do you like it?' asked Mary.

'I love it,' said Martha. 'It's beautiful in spring and
summer when it's full of wild flowers. I wouldn't live
anywhere else.'

New clothes   20

Mary looked at Martha in surprise.

'You are a strange servant,' Mary said.

Martha laughed. 'I know that,' she said. 'But this is
a strange house.'

'Who is going to dress me?' asked Mary.   25

'Can't you dress yourself?' Martha said.

'No,' answered Mary angrily. 'I never did in my life.
My Ayah dressed me.'

'Well,' said Martha, 'it's time you should learn.'

Suddenly Mary felt far away from everything she   30
understood. She threw herself down on the pillows
and began to cry. Martha came over to the bed.

'Don't cry,' she said softly. 'I didn't mean to upset you. Come on, get up and I'll help you get dressed. Then we'll go and have some breakfast.'

Martha brought Mary some new clothes that Mr Craven had bought for her.

'These are not mine,' said Mary. 'Mine are black.'

She looked at the thick white wool coat and dress. After a moment she said, 'These are nicer than mine.'

Dickon

Martha began to teach Mary how to dress herself. As she showed Mary what to do, she told her about her family.

'In our house, there are twelve of us and we're very poor. The children play on the moor all day. My brother Dickon is only twelve years old, but he's got his own pony.'

'Where did he get it?' asked Mary.

'He found it on the moor and began to make friends with it. He is kind and animals like him.'

Mary had never had an animal to love, and she had always wanted one. She began to feel interested in Dickon. When she went into the nursery next door, she found that it was like the room she had slept in. It was a grown-up's room, with sad old pictures on the walls. A table in the centre was prepared for breakfast. But Mary had never eaten very much.

'I don't want breakfast,' she said.

Martha looked at her in surprise. In her family the children were often hungry. She did not understand how someone could say no to good food.

'Go outside and play,' she said. 'Then perhaps you'll want your breakfast.'

One of the gardens is locked up

Mary went to the window. There were gardens and paths and big trees. Everything looked so cold. But there was nothing to do inside the house. Perhaps it would be better to go and see the gardens.

'Who will go with me?' she asked.

Martha stared.

'You'll go by yourself,' she answered. 'Dickon goes off on the moor by himself and plays for hours. That's how he made friends with the pony. 10

'If you go round that way, you'll come to the gardens,' she said, pointing to a gate in a wall made of bushes. 'But one of them is locked up.'

'Locked up?' said Mary in surprise.

Martha nodded. 'No one has been in it for ten 15 years,' she said.

'Why?' asked Mary.

'Mr Craven locked it when his wife died, and buried the key. He won't let anyone go inside. It was her garden.' 20

After Martha had gone, Mary walked down the path that led to the gate in the bushes. She thought about the garden which no one had been into for ten years. She wondered what it would be like. Would there be any flowers still alive in it? 25

THE ROBIN
THAT SHOWS THE WAY

Where is the locked garden?

There were many gardens with walls around them,
but they were not the locked garden because they
opened into each other. There were trees, but most
5 did not have leaves because it was still winter. Mary
thought that the gardens looked empty and ugly.

Soon she saw an old man walking through the
door leading from the second garden. He was
carrying a spade over his shoulder, and he did not
10 look pleased to see Mary. Mary was not pleased to
see him.

'What is this place?' she asked.

'One of the kitchen gardens where we grow our
vegetables,' he answered.

15 'What is that?' said Mary, pointing to a green door.

'Another garden. There's another on the other side
of the wall and there's the orchard on the other side
of that.'

'Can I go in them?' asked Mary.

20 'If you want to. But there's nothing to see.'

Mary went down the path and through the second
green door. There she found more walls and
vegetables. In the second wall, there was another
green door. Perhaps it led to the garden which no
25 one had seen for ten years. She tried the handle, and
the door opened quite easily.

The bird flies away

Mary walked through the door and found herself in an orchard: a garden full of trees. She could see the tops of trees on the other side of the far wall, but there was no green door leading to the other side.

Mary walked towards the far wall. Then the sound of a bird singing made her stop. She looked up and saw a red robin sitting on a high branch of one of the trees in the other garden. Mary had never seen a robin before. Hearing him sing almost made her sad face smile. Then the bird flew away.

'Will I ever see him again?' Mary asked herself. 20 'Perhaps he knows all about the secret garden. Perhaps that tree he was sitting on is in the secret garden. There was a wall around it and there was no door.'

She walked back into the first kitchen garden and 25 found the old man digging there.

'I have been to the other gardens,' she said. 'But there's no door from the orchard into that garden.'

'What garden?' he said, stopping his digging.

'The one on the other side of the wall,' answered 30 Mary. 'There were trees there — I saw the tops of them. A red bird was sitting on one of the trees, and he sang.'

The red robin

To her surprise, a smile slowly appeared on the old man's face. He turned to face towards the orchard, and began to whistle — a low, soft whistle.

5   The next moment a wonderful thing happened. The red robin flew into the garden and landed next to the old man's foot.

'Here he is,' said the old man. Laughing, he spoke to the bird as if he was speaking to a child. 'Where

10   have you been? I haven't seen you all day.'

The bird put his tiny head on one side. He looked up at him with his soft black eyes. He seemed happy to be near the old man. This gave Mary a strange feeling in her heart.

15   'Does he always come when you call him?' she asked.

The old man nodded. 'I've known him since he first came out of the other garden. The first time he flew over the wall, he was not strong enough to fly

20   back for a few days. Then we got friendly. When he went back, the rest of his family was gone and he was lonely. So he came back to me.'

'What kind of bird is he?' Mary asked.

'Don't you know? He's a red robin, and they're the most friendly birds. They're almost as friendly as dogs. Look, he knows we're talking about him.'

Ben Weatherstaff   5

Mary went a step nearer to the robin. She looked at him very hard.

'I'm lonely,' she said.

The old gardener pushed his hat back on his head. He stared at her for a minute.   10

'Are you the little girl from India?' he asked.

Mary nodded.

'Then I'm not surprised you're lonely. You'll get even lonelier living here.'

He began to dig again.   15

'What's your name?' Mary asked.

'Ben Weatherstaff,' he answered. 'I'm lonely myself except when he's with me,' he pointed to the robin. 'He's the only friend I've got.'

'I've got no friends at all,' said Mary. 'I never had.   20 My Ayah didn't like me and I never played with anyone.'

'You and I are very much the same,' said old Ben Weatherstaff. 'We are not pretty or friendly. And I guess that you have the same bad temper that I   25 have.'

Mary had never heard a servant talk like this before. She wondered if she was really like Ben Weatherstaff. She had never thought about her looks or her temper.

Suddenly the robin began to sing again. Mary   30 turned around and saw that he was sitting in a little apple tree. Ben Weatherstaff laughed.

The robin flies over the wall

'He wants to be friends with you,' he said.

'With me?' said Mary. She moved towards the tree softly and looked up. 'Will you be friends with me?' she said to the robin.

The bird ended his song and flew away.

Mary watched him. 'He is flying over the wall!' she cried out. 'He is flying into the orchard. Now he is flying across the other wall — into the garden where I first saw him.'

'He lives there,' said old Ben. 'He was born in the old rose trees there.'

'Rose trees,' said Mary. 'Are there rose trees?'

Ben Weatherstaff took up his spade again and began to dig.

'That was ten years ago,' he said.

'I would like to see them,' said Mary. 'Where is the door in that garden? There must be a door somewhere.'

'There was ten years ago, but there isn't now,' he said.

'But there must be a door!' cried Mary.

This seemed to make Ben angry. 'Forget about the door!' he said. 'I have work to do. Go away and play somewhere. I've got no more time to talk.'

Without looking at Mary or saying goodbye, he put his spade over his shoulder and walked away.

THE KEY TO THE GARDEN

How Mrs Craven died

Mary spent the next few days outdoors. Soon she began to feel hungry enough to eat her breakfast every morning.

'It's the air of the moor,' said Martha. 'You go on playing outdoors every day, and soon you won't look so thin and ill.'

In the evenings Mary talked to Martha.

'Why does Mr Craven hate the secret garden?' she asked.

'It was Mrs Craven's garden,' said Martha. 'She had it when they were first married, and she loved it. Mr and Mrs Craven used to shut themselves in there for hours and hours, reading and talking. Then one day Mrs Craven sat on the branch of one of the trees. The branch broke and she fell so badly that the next day she died. That's why he hates it. No one has ever gone in since, and he won't let anyone talk about it.'

Mary did not ask any more questions. She looked at the fire and listened to the wind. But then she began to hear a strange sound — almost like a child crying somewhere. It came from somewhere inside
5 the house but far away. Mary turned around and looked at Martha.

'Do you hear anyone crying?' she said.

'No,' said Martha quickly. 'It's the wind.'

'But listen,' said Mary. 'It's in the house — down
10 one of those long corridors.'

At that moment, the wind blew open the door of the room they were sitting in. They both jumped to their feet as the crying sound became clearer than ever.

15 'There!' said Mary. 'I told you so! It is someone crying, and it isn't a grown-up person.'

Martha ran and shut the door. 'It was the wind!' she said.

But they had both heard the sound of a door
20 closing far down the corridor.

Who is crying?

It rained for two whole days, and Mary could not go out. She spent most of her time walking down the corridors, past all the locked rooms. She heard the
25 crying sound again, but when she went to follow it, Mrs Medlock saw her.

'What are you doing here?' she said, taking Mary by the hand and pulling her away. 'What did I tell you?'

'I turned the wrong corner,' said Mary. 'And then I
30 heard someone crying.'

'You didn't hear anything!' said Mrs Medlock. 'Go back to your nursery. Stay there or I'll lock you up.'

On the third morning, the sun came out. A deep
blue sky appeared above the moor. Mary came out
into the first kitchen garden where Ben Weatherstaff
was working. He seemed happy to see the sun.

'Spring is coming,' he said. 'Can you smell it?'   5

'I can smell something nice,' said Mary.

Ben pointed to the ground. 'Under the earth the
flowers are getting ready to come out. The sun is
warming them.'

The robin flew over and landed beside her.   10

'Do you think he remembers me?' she said.

'He remembers everything in this garden,' said Ben.

Mary finds the key

Mary walked away, following the robin around the
long wall. A dog had dug up some earth, and the bird   15
landed beside it. Mary was watching the robin look
for food when she saw something almost buried in
the earth. It looked like a ring. When the robin flew
up into a tree near by, she put out her hand and
picked the ring up. At the end of the ring was an old   20
key.

Mary stood up and looked at it with an almost
frightened face.

'Perhaps it has been buried for ten years,' she
whispered. 'Perhaps it is the key to the garden. Now   25
I must find the door.'

She walked down the long path and around the
wall of the secret garden. She looked carefully, but
she could not see a door. Then the strong wind
moved all the trees and the green plants hanging   30
from the walls. Suddenly Mary saw a door handle
hidden beneath all the leaves. She ran forward, and

began to pull and push the leaves to one side. What
was this under her hands? It was square and made of
iron and her fingers found a hole in it. What could it
be?

5   It was the lock of the door which had been closed
for ten years. Mary put her hand in her pocket and
pulled out the key. Then she
put the key into the lock.
She turned it slowly.

Taking a long breath,
she looked behind her
up the long path to see if
anyone was coming. But no
one ever did come to this part of
15 the garden. Mary took another breath and pushed
back the door. It opened very slowly.

She went through the door, shutting it behind her.
She was standing inside the secret garden.

INSIDE THE
SECRET GARDEN

Mary works in the garden

It was the most lovely and strangest-looking place anyone could dream of. The high walls which shut it in were covered in climbing roses, but none had leaves or flowers. There were other trees and plants 5 in the garden, and they all seemed to grow into each other. Mary did not know if they were dead or alive. The garden looked different from other gardens which had not been left for so long. It looked different from any other place she had ever seen in 10 her life.

'How quiet it is!' she whispered.

Even the robin sat on his branch without moving or making a sound.

'I know why it is so quiet,' Mary whispered again. 15 'I am the first person who has spoken here for ten years.'

She moved around the garden, stepping slowly so that she would not wake anyone.

'I wonder if the plants are all dead,' she said. Then 20 she saw tiny green points coming from the black earth. She knelt down to look at them. 'Yes, these are tiny growing things. It isn't a completely dead garden. Even if the roses are dead, there are other things alive.' 25

Mary did not know anything about gardens. But she could see that there was so much grass that the green points did not have room to grow. She found a

piece of wood and knelt down. She dug out some of the grass. 'Now they can breathe,' she said to herself. 'I will clear all this old grass away. I haven't got time today, but I can come tomorrow.'

Mary wants a spade

Mary worked in the garden until it was time to go to her lunch. After she had eaten, she sat by the fire.

'I wish I had a little spade,' she said to Martha suddenly.

Martha laughed. 'What do you want a spade for?'

Mary looked at the fire and thought a little. The garden had to be a secret or Mr Craven would be very angry. Perhaps he would get a new key and lock it up for ever!

'This is such a big, lonely place,' she said slowly. 'So many places are shut up. There is no one to talk to here except you and Ben Weatherstaff. You have to do your work and Ben Weatherstaff won't speak to me often. If I have a little spade, I can dig somewhere as he does. I can even make a little garden if someone helps me.'

'That's a good idea,' said Martha. 'Dickon knows all about how to make things grow. He can get you the things you need in the village and bring them to you.'

'Then I shall meet him!' said Mary.

Martha looked pleased. 'Do you want to meet him?' she asked.

'Yes, I do. I never saw a boy that animals love. I want to see him very much,' Mary answered.

Mary felt tired after working in the garden, so she rested in front of the fire. Martha went to get some tea for them both. While she was away, Mary heard the sound of crying again. But when she told Martha, the young woman looked unhappy and almost ran out of the room.

'It's the strangest house anyone ever lived in,' Mary said, as she sat back in her chair. Fresh air and digging had made her feel very tired. She could not keep her eyes open.

Mary meets Dickon

The sun came out for nearly a week. Mary went into the secret garden and worked there every day. One morning, she was walking down the long path when she heard a strange whistling sound. She looked around and saw that a boy was sitting under a tree. He had his back against it and was playing on a wooden pipe. He was a funny-looking boy of about twelve. He looked very clean and his nose turned up. His cheeks were very red, and Mary had never seen such round blue eyes in a boy's face.

Beside the tree, two rabbits seemed to be watching him. When he saw Mary, he held up his hand and spoke to her in a low voice.

'Don't move,' he said. 'You'll frighten them.'

The boy stopped playing his pipe and got up very slowly.

'I'm Dickon,' he said.
'I know you are Miss Mary.'
He spoke to her as if they
were old friends. Mary knew
nothing about boys, and she felt a little funny.

'Did you get the spade?' she asked.

He nodded and a smile appeared all over his face.

'I've got all the garden tools you'll need. And some
flower seeds, too.'

10 He stopped and turned quickly.

'Where's that robin calling us from?' he said.

'Is he really calling us?' asked Mary.

'He's calling someone he's friends with. Look, there
he is in the bush! Who do you think his friend is?'

15 'Ben Weatherstaff,' answered Mary, 'but I think he
knows me a little.'

Dickon talks to the robin

Dickon moved slowly towards the bush. He made a
sound like a bird singing. The robin listened for a few
seconds. Then he answered with a song of his own.

Dickon turned and looked back at Mary.   5

'He does know you,' he said in a low voice. 'And
he likes you.'

Mary clapped her hands. 'Do you really think he
likes me?'

'He wouldn't come near you if he didn't,' answered   10
Dickon.

'Can you understand what birds say?' asked Mary.

Dickon laughed and rubbed his head.

'I think I do, and they think I do,' he said. 'I've
lived on the moor with them so long. Sometimes I   15
think that perhaps I'm a bird, or a rabbit, and I don't
know it.'

Still laughing he asked Mary to sit with him under
the tree. He began to talk about the flower seeds,
telling her what they looked like when they were   20
flowers. He told her how to plant them, feed them,
and water them.

'I'll plant them for you myself,' he said suddenly.
'Where is your garden?'

Mary did not know what to say, so for a whole   25
minute she said nothing. She felt terrible.

'You have got a garden, haven't you?' Dickon said.

Mary's face turned red and then white. She turned
her eyes towards him.

'Can you keep a secret?' she said slowly. 'It's a great   30
secret!'

'I'm keeping secrets for the animals all the time,'
said Dickon.

MARY AND MR CRAVEN

'I've stolen a garden'

Mary looked at him for a moment, and then she looked away.

'I've stolen a garden,' she said very fast. 'It isn't mine. It isn't anybody's. Nobody wants it, nobody cares for it, nobody ever goes into it. Perhaps everything in it is dead already!'

She began to feel hot and angry.

'They mustn't take it away from me when I care about it and they don't,' she said. 'They're letting it die!'

She put her head in her hands and began to cry.

'Don't cry!' said Dickon softly.

'Nothing belongs to me,' said Mary, through her tears. 'I found it myself and got into it myself.'

'Where is it?' asked Dickon in a low voice.

Mary dried her eyes and stood up.

'Come with me and I'll show you,' she said.

She led him down the long path and around the wall. When she showed Dickon the door, he was very surprised. Mary pushed it slowly open and they went in together.

'This is the secret garden,' she said. 'I'm the only person in the world who wants it to be alive.'

Dickon looked all round the garden.

'What a strange, pretty place!' he whispered. 'It's like something from a dream! I never thought I would ever see it.'

They are still alive

'Did you know about the garden?' said Mary, whispering because Dickon was whispering.

Dickon nodded.

'Martha told me,' he answered. 'I used to wonder   5
what it was like.'

Mary put her hand on his arm.

'Will there be roses?' she asked. 'I thought perhaps they were all dead.'

'No! Not all of them!' he answered.   10

Smiling, he took a knife from his pocket.

'There are lots of dead things that need to be cut out,' he said. 'Then we can help the living plants and trees grow. Let's go around the garden and see what we can do.'   15

They went from bush to bush and from tree to tree. Dickon was very strong and clever with his knife. Mary watched him and learned quickly how to cut away the dead wood from the trees. He also showed her how to use the garden tools.   20

After some time, they came to the place where Mary had cut the grass away.

'Who did that?' asked Dickon.

'I did it,' said Mary. 'But I don't know anything about gardens. Is it all right?'

'You have done a very good job!' said Dickon. 'And you've done so much work for such a little girl.'

'I'm growing fatter,' said Mary, 'and I'm growing stronger. I always used to be tired. When I dig, I'm not tired at all.'

'There's still a lot of work to do here!' said Dickon.

'Will you come again and help me to do it?' Mary begged. 'Please come, Dickon!'

'I'll come every day if you want me to,' he answered. 'Waking up this garden will be the best fun I've ever had in my life!'

Mr Craven is back

When Mary got back to the house, her lunch was waiting on the table.

'You're late,' said Martha. 'Where have you been?'

'I've seen Dickon!' said Mary.

'What do you think of him?' asked Martha.

'I think — I think he's beautiful!' said Mary.

Martha laughed.

'Well, he's the best boy I know,' she said. 'But I never thought him good-looking.'

Mary ate her lunch as quickly as she could and got up from the table. Martha put her hand out to stop her.

'Mr Craven came back from London this morning and he wants to see you,' she said.

At that moment, Mrs Medlock walked in.

'Go and brush your hair,' she told Mary. 'Mr Craven has sent me here to bring you to his room.'

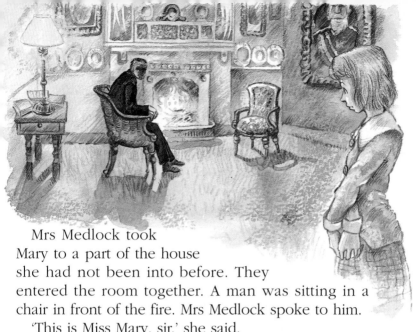

Mrs Medlock took
Mary to a part of the house
she had not been into before. They
entered the room together. A man was sitting in a
chair in front of the fire. Mrs Medlock spoke to him.

'This is Miss Mary, sir,' she said.

'Can I have some earth?'

When Mrs Medlock left the room, Mary stood waiting.
She could see that the man in the chair had high,
crooked shoulders. He turned his head and spoke to
her.   10

'Come here!' he said.

When Mary went to him, she saw that he was not
ugly. But what an unhappy face he had! He rubbed
his face as he looked at her. He did not know what to   15
do with her.

'You are very thin,' he said.

'I am getting fatter,' Mary answered.

'I was going to send you to school,' he said. 'But I
forgot.'   20

'Please don't send me to school yet!' said Mary. The
idea of going away from the secret garden made her
want to cry.

Mr Craven rubbed his head again and stared at her. 'What do you want to do?' he asked.

'I want to play outdoors,' Mary answered. 'It makes me hungry, and I'm getting fatter.'

Mr Craven nodded.

'Perhaps you need to get stronger before you go to school,' he said. 'Play outdoors as much as you like. Do you want any toys or books?'

'Can I have some earth?' asked Mary in a low voice.

Mary can have her earth

Mr Craven looked very surprised.

'Earth!' he repeated. 'What do you mean?'

'To plant seeds in,' said Mary. 'To make things grow and see them come alive.'

'Do you care a lot about gardens?' he said slowly.

'I didn't know about them in India,' said Mary. 'I was always ill and tired. And it was so hot. But here it is different.'

Mr Craven got up and began to walk across the room. When he stopped and spoke to her, his dark eyes looked almost soft and kind.

'You can have as much earth as you want,' he said. 'You make me think of someone else who loved the earth and things that grow.'

'May I take it from anywhere — if it's not wanted?'

'Anywhere,' he answered. 'But you must go now. I am tired.' He touched the bell to call Mrs Medlock. 'Goodbye. I shall be away all summer.'

THE CRYING
IN THE CORRIDOR

A message from Dickon

Mary ran as quickly as she could to the secret garden. She could not find Dickon there, but his garden tools were under a tree. The secret garden was empty again.

She felt very sad, but then she saw a piece of paper 5 on top of a rose bush. She picked it up and saw a sort of picture on it. When she looked more carefully, she saw that the picture was of the red robin. Below the picture were the words, 'I will come back.'

That night Mary woke up to the sound of wind and 10 rain. The rain made her feel sad and angry, and she could not go back to sleep again. After a few minutes, she noticed that there was another sound.

'That isn't the wind,' she said in a loud whisper. 'It is that crying I heard before. I am going to find out 15 what it is. Everybody is in bed and I don't care about Mrs Medlock.'

Mary took the candle by her bed and went softly out of the room. The corridor looked very long and dark, but she was too excited to be frightened. Soon 20 she came to a door with a light coming from under it. Mary pushed it open and walked in.

'Are you a ghost?'

It was a big room with old, beautiful things in it. There was a fire burning at the back of the room, and 25 a big bed in the corner. Lying on the bed was a boy.

He was crying into his pillow. He had a thin, very white face, big eyes and long hair. He looked like a boy who had been ill, but he did not look in pain. He seemed to be crying as he was tired or angry.

Mary stood near the door with her candle in her hand. She wondered if she was dreaming. She moved slowly across the room towards the bed. As she got nearer, the boy saw the light. He turned his head on the pillow and stared at her.

'Who are you?' he said at last in a frightened whisper. 'Are you a ghost?'

'No, I am not,' Mary answered. 'Are you one?'

'No,' he replied after a moment. 'I am Colin Craven. Who are you?'

20 'I am Mary Lennox. Mr Craven is my uncle.'

'He is my father,' said the boy.

Why Colin was crying

'Your father!' said Mary. 'No one ever told me he had a boy! Why didn't they?'

25 'Come here,' he said, staring at her with his strange, grey eyes.

She came close to the bed and he put his hand out and touched her.

'Where did you come from?' he said.

30 'From my own room. I couldn't sleep because of the wind and I heard someone crying. I wanted to find out who it was. What were you crying for?'

'Because I couldn't go to sleep either. And my head hurt. Tell me your name again,' he answered.

'Mary Lennox. Did no one ever tell you I had come to live here?'

'No,' he answered. 'They were too frightened to.'

'Why?' asked Mary.

'Because I won't let people see me. I am always ill and I don't like people talking about me. If I live, I shall have a crooked back, but I won't live.'

'Oh what a strange house this is!' Mary said. 'Everything is a kind of secret. Rooms and gardens are locked up! Have you been locked up?'

'No. I stay in this room because I don't want to move out of it. It makes me very tired.'

'Does your father come and see you?'

'Sometimes. Often when I am asleep. He doesn't want to see me.'

'Why?'

Colin looked angry.

'My mother died soon after I was born, and it makes him sad to look at me. He thinks I don't know, but I've heard people talking. He almost hates me.'

'What garden?'

'He hates the garden, because she died there,' said Mary to herself.

'What garden?' the boy asked.

'Oh! Just — just a garden she used to like,' Mary said quickly. 'Have you always been here?'

'Nearly always. I used to wear an iron thing to keep my back straight, but then a doctor came from London and told them to take it off. He said I needed fresh air, but I hate fresh air! I don't want to go out.'

'I didn't when I first came here,' said Mary.

Colin wanted to know all about Mary.

'How old are you?' he asked.

'I am ten,' answered Mary. Then without thinking
she said, 'And so are you.'

'How do you know that?'

'Because soon after you were born, the garden
door was locked. And it has been locked for ten
years.'

Colin half sat up.

'What garden door was locked?' he said.

'It's the garden that Mr Craven hates,' said Mary
carefully. 'He locked the door and buried the key. No
one has been allowed to go into it for ten years.'

Colin wants to see the garden

But it was too late to be careful. Colin wanted to
know all about the garden.

'Have you asked the gardeners where the garden
is?' he asked.

'They won't talk about it,' said Mary.

'I will make them,' said Colin. 'They all know that if
I live, Misselthwaite Manor will belong to me.'

Mary had not known that she herself had been
spoiled. But she could see that this boy had been.

'Don't you think you will live?' she asked.

'No,' he answered in the same calm voice.

'Do you want to live?' Mary asked.

'No,' he answered, in a tired voice. 'But I don't
want to die. When I feel ill, I lie here and think about
it until I cry. Let's talk about something else. Tell me
about the garden. Don't you want to see it?'

'Yes,' answered Mary in a low voice.

'I want to see it,' said Colin. 'I want the key dug up and the door opened. Then I will make them take me there in my chair.'

A secret

'Oh no!' cried Mary. 'Don't do that!'   5

'Why not? You said you wanted to see it.'

'I do,' she answered, 'but if you make them open the door, it will never be a secret again.'

'A secret,' he said. 'What do you mean?'

'If we found the garden, nobody else would know   10
about it. It would be our secret garden. We could plant seeds and make it come alive. If you don't tell the gardeners,' said Mary carefully, 'I think I can find out how to get in some time.'

'I would like that,' he said very slowly. 'I would not   15
mind fresh air in a secret garden.'

'What will Mrs Medlock do if she finds out I've been here?' Mary asked after a while.

'She will do what I tell her to do,' he answered. 'And I will tell her that I want you to come and talk to   20
me every day. I am glad you came.'

'So am I,' said Mary. 'I will come as often as I can.'

'I think you should be a secret, too,' he said. 'Do you know Martha? She looks after me when my nurse is away.'   25

So that was why Martha had not wanted to answer Mary's questions!

'Martha can tell you when to come and see me,' said Colin, his eyes closing.

Mary got up softly and left the room without a   30
sound.

THE DIFFICULT BOY

Colin wants to see Mary

Martha was very frightened when Mary first told her about seeing Colin.

'I shall lose my job!' she cried.

5 'You won't lose your job,' said Mary. 'We talked for a long time and he said that he was glad I came. But I think he's a very spoiled boy,' said Mary.

'He's the most difficult boy in the world!' said Martha. 'He has been ill a lot of the time. He nearly 10 died.'

'Do you think he will die?' asked Mary.

'The doctor from London said that he takes too much medicine and does not get enough fresh air. Perhaps the way he lives makes him ill.'

15 Mary sat and looked at the fire.

'Perhaps it would do him good to go out into a garden and watch things growing. It did me good.'

'They tried to show him the roses once,' said Martha. 'And one of the gardeners looked at him. He 20 got so angry and cried so much that he was ill all night.'

'If he ever gets angry with me, I'll never go and see him again,' said Mary.

Later that morning Martha went to see Colin. She 25 returned with a smile on her face.

'You have done some magic on him,' she said. 'He is sitting up on his sofa with his picture books. And he wants to see you.'

'Let's talk about Dickon'

Mary told Colin about Dickon.

'He is twelve years old,' she explained. 'And he is not like anyone else in the world. He can speak to animals and birds. He knows everything about the moor. I think he can do magic!'

'Does he like the moor?' said Colin. 'How can he when it's such a big, ugly place?'

'It's the most beautiful place,' said Mary. 'Thousands of lovely things grow on it.'

'You never see anything if you are ill,' said Colin.

'You can't if you stay in your room,' said Mary.

'I can't go on the moor! I am going to die!'

'How do you know?' said Mary. She didn't like the way he was always talking about dying.

'Because I hear them talking. It's what everyone wants. Even my father.'

'I don't believe he does,' said Mary. 'I think you will live if you want to live. But let's not talk about it.'

So they talked about Dickon and the robin, and began to laugh. They enjoyed themselves very much, and they forgot that it was still raining outside.

It continued to rain for nearly a week. Every day Mary told Colin more about Dickon.

'You know I hate people to see me,' said Colin. 'But I think Dickon is the only boy in the world I would like to see.'

Mary meets Captain and Soot

On the first morning when the sky was blue again, Mary woke up very early. She put her hand out of the window and held it in the sun.

'It's warm!' she said. 'It will make the flowers grow. I must go straight to the secret garden.'

She ran all the way to the garden. Dickon was already there.

5 'Oh, Dickon!' she cried out. 'How could you get here so early! The sun has only just got up!'

Dickon laughed.

'I was up long before the sun. The world is ready to begin again this morning.'

A baby fox came out from behind a tree and moved close to Dickon. Then a bird flew down and landed on his shoulder.

'This is Captain,' he said, rubbing the little red animal's head. 'And this one on my shoulder is Soot. Soot flew across the moor with me.'

'Oh, Dickon!' Mary said. 'I'm so happy!'

Later she told him about Colin.

20 'It would be good for him to come out here with us,' said Dickon. 'Look what it has done for you!'

'I'm getting fatter and fatter every day,' said Mary. 'But Colin is afraid that he is going to have a crooked back like his father. That's why he never sits up.'

25 'If he is out here, he won't be thinking about having a crooked back,' said Dickon.

Colin and Mary get angry

Mary worked with Dickon in the secret garden all day. When she arrived back at the house, Martha was waiting for her.

'Colin is very upset,' said Martha. 'He was waiting for you to come and see him.'

Mary went to Colin's room, and found him lying on his back in bed. He did not turn his head towards her as she came in.

'Why didn't you get up?' she said.

'I did get up this morning when I thought you were coming,' he answered, without looking at her. 'My back hurt and I was tired. Why didn't you come?'

'I was working in the garden with Dickon.'

'I won't let that boy come here!' he shouted.

'If you send Dickon away, I'll never come into this room again,' she answered, losing her temper.

'You are a selfish girl!' cried Colin.

'What are you?' said Mary. 'You're more selfish than I am. You're the most selfish boy I ever saw.'

'I'm not!' shouted Colin. A big tear ran down his cheek.

'I'm sure there is a lump growing on my back,' he continued. 'And I am going to die.'

'You're not going to die!' said Mary.

Colin had never heard such a thing said before. He was both angry and a little pleased.

'You know I am!' he cried.

'I don't believe it!' said Mary. 'You just say that to make people feel sorry for you!'

'Get out of my room!' he shouted. He picked up his pillow and threw it at her.

'I'm going,' said Mary. 'And I won't come back!'

A LUMP ON THE BACK

The noise in the night

That night Mary woke up to hear a terrible noise. Doors were opened and shut. There were people hurrying along the corridors. Someone was crying and screaming in a horrible way.

'It's Colin,' she said. 'How terrible it sounds!'

Mary put her hands over her ears, but still she could hear the terrible screams. She jumped out of bed.

'Someone stop him doing that!' she cried out.

Mary ran down the corridor towards Colin's room. As she got closer, her temper became worse. She pushed the door open and ran across the room to the bed.

'You stop!' she shouted. 'I hate you! Everybody hates you! I wish everybody would run out of the house and let you scream yourself to death.'

A nice girl should not say these things. But hearing them was the best possible thing for Colin. Nobody had ever tried to shout at him before.

Colin turned to look at Mary. His face looked terrible, but Mary did not care.

'If you scream another scream,' she said, 'I'll scream too! I can scream louder than you can. I'll frighten you!'

Tears ran down Colin's face, and he was shaking all over.

'I can't stop!' he cried. 'I felt the lump! I shall have a crooked back and die!'

Is there a lump?

Colin turned on his face and began to cry again. But he did not scream.

'You didn't feel a lump!' said Mary angrily. 'There's nothing wrong with your back. Turn over and let me look at it.' 5

For a moment Colin did not answer. Then he turned and called to Martha. She had come quietly into the room.

'Show her!' he said. 'She'll see my crooked back then.'

It was a poor, thin back, but Mary looked at it very carefully.

'There's not a lump there at all!' she said at last. 'There's not a lump as big as a pin.'

'I didn't know,' said Martha, 'that he thought he had a lump. His back is weak because he won't try to sit up.'

Colin turned and looked at Martha.

5 'Do you think I could live to grow up?'

Martha nodded.

'You will if you do what is right. You must not get upset, and you should spend more time in the fresh air.'

10 Colin was weak and tired from crying, but he was no longer angry. Mary was not angry either. She realized that Colin had screamed because he had been frightened. While she had been with Dickon in the secret garden, Colin had spent the afternoon 15 thinking about dying.

Colin turned to Mary. 'I'll go out with you,' he said. 'Perhaps Dickon will come and push my chair. I'd love to see him and his animals.'

'Can I trust you?'

20 The next day Mary worked with Dickon in the secret garden. Later she went to see Colin. They talked about how Dickon was friends with all the animals and birds.

'I wish I was friends with things,' said Colin. 'I never had anything to be friends with, and I don't like 25 people.'

'Do you like me?' asked Mary.

'Yes, I do,' he answered. 'It's funny but I do like you.'

'Ben Weatherstaff said I was like him,' said Mary. 30 'He said that we were both bad-tempered. I think you are like him, too. But I am not as bad-tempered as I was before I knew the robin and Dickon.'

'Did you hate people before?'

'Yes,' said Mary.

Colin put out his thin hand and touched her.

'Mary,' he said, 'I am sorry for what I said about Dickon. I really would like to see him.'

Mary looked at him for a moment.

'Can I trust you?' she said slowly. 'I trusted Dickon because birds trusted him. Can I trust you for sure?'

'Yes!' whispered Colin. 'You can trust me! I promise!'

'Well, Dickon will come to see you tomorrow morning, and he'll bring his animals with him.'

Colin cried out in delight.

'But that's not all,' Mary went on. 'I have found the door into the secret garden.'

'Oh! Mary! Shall I see the secret garden? Shall I live to get into it?' said Colin, taking Mary's hands and pulling her towards him.

'Of course you'll live to see it!' said Mary. 'Don't be silly!'

MAGIC

Colin goes to the secret garden

A few weeks later, Dickon and Mary took Colin out to
show him the gardens. Dickon pushed Colin, who sat
back on the cushions in his wheelchair. Mary walked
5   beside them.

'That is the garden where Ben Weatherstaff works,'
said Mary.

'Is it?' said Colin.

A few yards more and Mary whispered again.

10   'This is where the robin flew over the wall,' she
said.

'Is it?' cried Colin. 'Oh! I wish he'd come again!'

'And here is the door to the secret garden. Dickon,
push him in quickly!' said Mary.

15   Dickon did it with one strong push. Colin fell back
against his cushions. Then he cried out with delight
when he saw inside
the garden.

He looked round and round at all the flowers and trees. The plants were coming back to life because of Dickon and Mary.

'I shall get well!' he cried out. 'Mary! Dickon! I shall get well. I shall live for ever!' 5

Colin pushed himself around the garden while Dickon and Mary worked.

'I would love to walk and dig like you do,' he said. 'But my legs are very thin and weak. I am afraid to stand on them.' 10

'When you stop being afraid, you'll stand on them,' said Dickon kindly. 'And the secret· garden will soon stop you being afraid.'

The afternoon was ending and the sun was going down. There was silence as Dickon and Mary worked 15 and Colin watched.

Then Colin looked up and saw something.

Ben on a ladder

'Who is that man?' Colin called out in surprise.

Dickon and Mary jumped to their feet. There was 20 Ben Weatherstaff's angry face staring at them over the wall. He was at the top of a ladder.

'What do you think you are doing in there?' he shouted.

Mary ran over to the wall. 25

'Ben Weatherstaff,' she called up to him. 'It was the robin who showed me the way in here.'

This made Ben even more angry. 'The robin has nothing to do with this. You are a bad child!' he shouted. 30

Suddenly Colin turned to Dickon. 'Push me over there!' he said. 'Stop right in front of him.'

What Ben Weatherstaff saw next was a boy coming towards him in a wheelchair. He looked like a young prince.

'Do you know who I am?' asked Colin.

'Have I got crooked legs?'

Ben stared at him for a moment with his mouth open. At last he said in a strange voice, 'I can see your mother's eyes staring out of your face. But I don't know what you are doing here. You've got a crooked body and can't do anything.'

Colin sat up straight in his chair. His face went red. 'I haven't got a crooked body!' he cried out.

Ben Weatherstaff put his hand to his mouth in surprise. 'You haven't got a crooked back?' he asked.

'No!' shouted Colin.

'And you haven't got crooked legs?'

This made Colin completely lose his temper. But this time he did not cry. He started to push himself out of the wheelchair.

'He can do it!' cried Mary. 'I know he can!'

Dickon held Colin's arm. The thin legs and thin feet came down onto the grass. Colin was standing up!

'Look at me!' he shouted at Ben Weatherstaff. 'Have I got a crooked back? Have I got crooked legs?'

'No,' said Ben Weatherstaff, tears running down his face. 'The lies that people tell are terrible.'

Colin walks

Dickon held Colin's arms strongly, but the boy was still standing straight. Colin looked Ben Weatherstaff in the face.

'You must obey me,' he said, 'when my father is away. This is my garden and it is a secret. Come down from that ladder and go out to the long path. Miss Mary will meet you and bring you here.'

Mary went out to meet Ben Weatherstaff. Colin turned to Dickon.

'I can stand!' he said.

'You've stopped being afraid,' answered Dickon.

'Yes, I've stopped,' said Colin.   10

Suddenly Colin remembered something that Mary had said about Dickon.

'Are you doing magic?' he asked. 'Like you do with the animals?'

Dickon smiled.   15

'You are doing magic yourself,' Dickon said. 'It's the same magic that made these flowers grow out of the earth.'

Colin looked down at the beautiful white and purple flowers. Then he stood up even straighter.   20

'I'm going to walk to that tree,' he said, pointing to one a few feet from him. 'I'll be standing when Ben Weatherstaff comes here.'

THE GARDEN
THAT COMES ALIVE

Colin talks to Ben

Colin walked to the tree, and Dickon only had to
hold his arm. At the same time Mary met Ben on the
long path. Colin was standing by the tree when Mary
5 and Ben came through the door in the wall.

'What work do you do in the gardens, Mr Weatherstaff?'
he asked.

'Anything I'm told to do,' answered old Ben. 'I've
worked here since your mother was alive.'

10 'My mother?' said Colin quietly. He looked around
the garden. 'This was her garden, wasn't it?'

Ben looked around too. 'Yes, it was,' he said. 'She
liked it very much.'

'I've come here before'

15 'It is my garden now,' said Colin. 'I like it and shall
come here every day. But it is to be a secret. I shall
send for you sometimes to help, but you must come
when no one can see you.'

Ben Weatherstaff smiled.

20 'I've come here before when no one has seen me.'

'What!' cried Colin. 'When?'

'The last time I was here,' said Ben, looking round,
'was about two years ago.'

Dickon laughed.

25 'I knew someone had been here!' he cried. 'That
was why so many plants were still alive.'

Soon all four of them were laughing. As the sun went down on that lovely afternoon, Colin was standing on his two feet — laughing.

Colin gets stronger

Over the next few weeks Colin, Dickon and Mary   5
worked in the secret garden every day. Flowers of every colour were growing up, and now there was a whole family of red robins. When it rained, the children looked round all the secret rooms inside the house.

Colin began to look and feel better. Like Mary, he was getting stronger every day. Soon he could dig the earth like the others, and Dickon helped him to become stronger. Then he began to learn how to walk — slowly at first, but better and better each day. Colin said that the 'magic' of the secret garden was helping him do something he had not thought possible. One day he stopped digging and called over to the other two.

'Mary! Dickon!' he cried. 'Just look at me!'

Dickon and Mary were looking at him very hard.   30

'I'm well! I shall live for ever and ever!' he cried out.

Mr Craven comes back

While the secret garden was coming alive, and two children were coming alive with it, Mr Craven was far away. For ten years he had been travelling around Europe, trying to forget his broken heart. Then, on the same day that Colin cried out, 'I shall live for ever!', Mr Craven dreamt that his wife was standing in her special garden at Misselthwaite Manor.

'Come home,' she called, 'to the garden.'

The next morning he decided to go home. During the long train and boat journey, he thought that he had not been a good father at all.

Back to the secret garden

When he arrived back at Misselthwaite Manor, Mr Craven went straight to the secret garden. As he got closer, a boy came running out of the garden and nearly knocked him over. Mr Craven put his hands out and caught the boy.

When he held him away to look at him, he could not believe what he saw.

He was a tall boy and a good-looking one. A boy full of life.

'Father,' said the boy, 'I'm Colin. You can't believe it! I almost can't believe it myself!'

Colin put his hand on his father's arm.

'It was the garden that did it!' he cried. 'And Mary and Dickon and the robin! And the magic! No one knows. We kept it a secret to tell you when you came. I'm well!'

Mr Craven put his hand on both the boy's shoulders and held him still.

'Take me into the garden, my boy,' he said at last. 'And tell me all about it.'

And so Colin led his father into the garden. It now looked more beautiful than ever. Mr Craven sat with Mary, Dickon and the animals, and listened to Colin tell his story.

'Now,' said Colin at the end of the story, 'it does not need to be a secret any more. I shall never need my wheelchair again. I shall walk back to the house with you, Father.'

QUESTIONS AND ACTIVITIES

CHAPTER 1

Some of these sentences are true and some are false. Which ones are true? What is wrong with the false ones?

1 Mary Lennox lived in Italy.
2 Her mother was very ugly.
3 Her father was never ill.
4 Mary was very bad-tempered.
5 Mary hid in the garden.
6 Mary's only visitor was a snake.
7 Mary travelled to England with a soldier.
8 Mrs Medlock wore a yellow dress and a red hat.

CHAPTER 2

Put the sentences in the right order to say what happens in this part of the story; the first one is correct.

1 Mary and Mrs Medlock said goodbye to the soldier's wife.
2 Mrs Medlock woke Mary.
3 Mrs Medlock told Mary about Misselthwaite Manor.
4 The coach went through the village.
5 They got into the coach.
6 The rain stopped.
7 Mary fell asleep.
8 The coach went up a hill onto the moor.

CHAPTER 3

Choose the right words to say what happens in this part of the story.

They drove through some (1) **gates/doors** and down a road with (2) **houses/trees** on both sides. At last they came to the (3) **prettiest/longest** house that Mary had ever seen. (4) **Mr Craven/A servant** opened the door, and Mrs Medlock took Mary up (5) **in a lift/the stairs** to her room. The room was

(6) **dark/bright**, with a fire and some (7) **food/toys** on a table. The next morning (8) **Martha/Mrs Craven** came into the room to light the fire. From the window Mary could see the (9) **railway/moor**. Mary thought that Martha was a strange (10) **teacher/servant**. Then Martha brought her some new (11) **clothes/books** and told her about (12) **Colin/Dickon**.

CHAPTER 4

Fill the gaps using each of these words once to say what happens in the story: **door, locked, opened, gardener, buried, digging, friendly**.

Mary knew that Mr Craven had (1) _____ one of the gardens and (2) _____ the key. In one garden she saw a green (3) _____ and she thought that it might lead to the secret garden. But the door was not locked and it (4) _____ easily. She found herself in an orchard. Mary went back to the old (5) _____ who was (6) _____ in the first kitchen garden. She asked him about the secret garden but he was not very (7) _____.

CHAPTER 5

Something is wrong in the underlined part of each sentence. What should it be?

1 Mrs Craven <u>stood next to one of the trees</u>. The branch broke and she fell.
2 When Mary heard a strange sound, she thought <u>it was the wind</u>.
3 Mary spent most of her time <u>working in the garden</u> when it rained for two whole days.
4 When Mary heard the crying sound again, she <u>went to see Mrs Medlock</u>.
5 Mary was <u>looking for food</u> when she saw something in the earth.
6 At last Mary found the key to the secret garden, <u>but she could not find the door</u>.
7 Mary saw <u>a spade hidden beneath the earth</u>. It was square and made of iron.

CHAPTER 6

Put the beginnings of these sentences with the right endings.

1 Mary did not know if the plants …	(a)	he was playing a wooden pipe.
2 There was so much grass …	(b)	dig her own little garden.
3 Mary worked in the garden …	(c)	were dead or alive.
4 Mary wanted a spade to …	(d)	what birds and animals said.
5 When Mary met Dickon, …	(e)	that the green points could not breathe.
6 Dickon could understand …	(f)	until it was time to go for her lunch.

CHAPTER 7

The letters in these words are mixed up. What should they be? (The first one is 'door'.)

When Mary showed Dickon the (1) **ordo** to the secret garden, he was very surprised. He told Mary that not all the (2) **orses** were (3) **edad**, and that he would come (4) **yvere** day to help her work in the (5) **radgne**. When Mary went back to the house, Mrs Medlock took her to see Mr Craven. Mary asked Mr Craven for some (6) **etrah** to plant (7) **desse** in. He let her have what she wanted.

CHAPTER 8

*Write the right name in each gap. Choose from: **Colin**, **Mary**, **Dickon**, **Mr Craven**, **Martha**.*

(1) _____ drew a picture of a robin for Mary, and left it in the secret garden. Later that night (2) _____ heard the sound of crying coming from another part of the house. The boy who was crying was called (3) _____ and he was the son of (4) _____. Mr Craven wanted to keep Colin a secret, so (5) _____ did not like answering questions about him.

CHAPTER 9

Choose the right words to say what happens in this part of the story.

Mary wanted to keep the garden (1) **locked/a secret**. Colin said that he (2) **would like/would not like** to visit the garden. Martha said that Colin was a very (3) **difficult/nice** boy. Colin thought that he was going to (4) **die/live for ever**, but the doctor from London said he needed (5) **magic/fresh air**.

CHAPTER 10

Which sentences are true? What is wrong with the false ones?

1 Mary woke up because of the wind.
2 Mary ran to Colin's room.
3 Mary told Colin to stop crying.
4 Colin thought that there was a lump on his head.
5 Mary found a big lump.

CHAPTER 11

Put the words at the end of each sentence in the right order.

1 Mary and Dickon took Colin   [gardens] [see] [the] [to].
2 Ben Weatherstaff stood on a   [looked] [ladder] [and] [garden] [the] [into].
3 Colin got out of the   [and] [wheelchair] [stood] [feet] [his] [on].
4 Mary went out   [Ben] [meet] [to] [old].

CHAPTER 12

Choose the right words to put in the gaps to say what this part of the story is about: ***animals, someone, good-looking, work***.

Colin asked Ben about his (1) _____ in the garden. Ben said that he had been in the secret garden after Mr Craven had locked it. Dickon said that he knew that (2) _____ had done some work in the garden. Mr Craven came back and found Colin tall and (3) _____. Colin told him about the secret garden and took him to see it. Mr Craven sat with Mary, Dickon and the (4) _____, and listened to Colin tell his story.